A Ladybird Book

The Easter Story

Text by Jenny Robertson
Illustrations by Alan Parry

The leaders of the Jews, who hated Jesus,
managed to capture him at last. All night they
tried to find a reason to have him killed.

At dawn the High Priest asked, 'Are you
the Son of God?'

'Yes, I am,' Jesus replied.

'He claims to be God! That's against our
holy law!' cried the High Priest.

'He's guilty!' the others agreed. 'He must
die.'

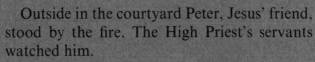
Outside in the courtyard Peter, Jesus' friend,
stood by the fire. The High Priest's servants
watched him.

'You were with Jesus,' said one.

'I don't know what you mean!' stammered Peter.

'He *is* one of Jesus' friends,' a maid insisted.

Another servant agreed, but each time Peter said he had never known Jesus. Then a cock crowed. Peter remembered how Jesus had warned him that, before the cock crowed that morning, he would say three times that he did not know Jesus. He rushed outside and cried bitterly.

'We have caught a real trouble maker,' the Jewish leaders informed the Roman Governor, Pontius Pilate. 'He stirs up our people against the Romans. He even calls himself a king.'

'Do you hear what they are saying?' Pilate asked Jesus. 'Are you a king?'

'So you say,' answered Jesus, but he would not say anything more.

Pilate looked helplessly at his prisoner. He knew Jesus was innocent, but the priests wanted him killed.

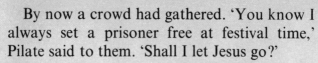

By now a crowd had gathered. 'You know I always set a prisoner free at festival time,' Pilate said to them. 'Shall I let Jesus go?'

'No!' shouted the people. 'Free Barabbas!' Barabbas was a bandit.

Pilate was afraid of the crowd, so, while Barabbas went free, he handed Jesus over to the soldiers, who beat him cruelly. They made a crown from thorns and forced it on to Jesus'

head. Then they wrapped a purple cloak round him, and bowed to him, jeering, 'Long live the King!'

At last Pilate took Jesus out to the crowd. 'What do you want me to do with this man?' he asked. 'He has done nothing to deserve death.'

'The cross!' yelled the people, persuaded by the priests. 'Hang him on the cross!'

So Jesus was led away to die. He had to carry his own cross. It was heavy, and his shoulders were torn and bleeding from the soldiers' whips. On the road he stumbled and fell under the weight. Then the soldiers seized a man called

Simon, who had come from North Africa to keep the festival in Jerusalem. They forced him to carry Jesus' heavy load. Simon remembered that cross for the rest of his life.

Beyond the city walls was a place called 'Skull Hill'. There they laid Jesus down on the cross and hammered nails through his hands and feet.

Jesus said, 'Father, forgive them. They don't understand what they are doing.'

Two robbers were nailed to crosses on either side of him. The soldiers, to pass the time, threw dice to see who would win the clothes which Jesus wore. A large crowd watched, while their leaders jeered, 'Get yourself off the cross, King!' One of the robbers joined in, but the other said, 'We are getting what we deserve, but this man hasn't done anything wrong.' Turning to Jesus, he said, 'Remember me when you come back as king.'

'Today you shall be in Paradise with me,' Jesus answered firmly.

It was nine o'clock when they nailed Jesus to the cross. At midday the sky grew black.

Jesus called out into the darkness, 'My God, my God, why have you deserted me?'

Some people heard him and wondered if, even now, God would rescue him.

Jesus had little strength left. 'I'm so thirsty!' he gasped. Soldiers soaked a sponge with sour wine and lifted it up to moisten his lips.

'Everything is finished!' Jesus cried. He bowed his head and died.

Two of his secret followers begged Pilate for Jesus' body. They wrapped it in linen cloths and took it to a garden where there was a new grave cut in the rock.

Early on Sunday morning Mary, one of Jesus' friends, went sadly to the grave. With a shock she saw that it stood open.

Mary ran to fetch Peter and John, another friend.

Together they raced to the grave. It was empty. Only the linen cloths lay on the ground. Puzzled, the men left, but Mary stayed, crying.

'Why are you crying?' she heard a man ask.

She thought it was the gardener. 'Sir,' she said, 'do you know where his body is?'

'Mary!' said the man, and then she knew. It was Jesus!

'Master!' she cried happily, feeling her sadness turning to joy.

'Go and tell my friends I am alive.' said Jesus joyfully.

Mary ran back to Jesus' friends, but they wouldn't believe her. 'Alive? It can't be true!' they muttered.

That afternoon two of the men left Jerusalem for nearby Emmaus, talking as they went. A stranger caught up with them.

'What are you discussing?' he asked.

'Haven't you heard about Jesus of Nazareth?' they said. 'We thought he was the one sent by God to help us, but he has been put to death. Now some women are saying he is alive again. Certainly his body has disappeared. It's very puzzling.'

'But don't our holy writings say that God's promised King must die and rise again?' asked the stranger, and he explained many things to them.

They were so interested they asked him to stay with them. At supper he took the bread, thanked God, and broke it, just as Jesus used to do. Then they saw it *was* Jesus, but he disappeared immediately.

The two men rushed straight back to Jerusalem. They wanted to tell the others, but their friends had their own exciting news to tell – 'Jesus is alive! Peter saw him!'

'We know, he met us on the road and talked to us!' the two men answered.

Suddenly Jesus was in the room with them. They were terrified, but Jesus quickly spoke to them.

'I'm not a ghost!' he told them. 'Touch me, you can't touch ghosts!'

They still could hardly believe it. Yet there he was, smiling, showing his hands and feet which had been nailed to the cross.

'Have you any food, friends?' he asked. They gave him some cooked fish, and watched, amazed, as he ate.

'Soon you must go and tell everyone that I died and came alive again so that their sins could be forgiven,' said Jesus. 'But first you must wait until God sends the Holy Spirit to be with you in my place. He will give you the help you need.'

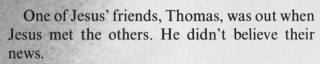

One of Jesus' friends, Thomas, was out when Jesus met the others. He didn't believe their news.

'Unless I actually touch his scars, I won't believe Jesus is alive!' Thomas said. Eight days later Thomas was with the others, and Jesus came again.

'Look, Thomas,' he said, 'here are the marks of the nails. Touch these scars and believe.'

Thomas fell to his knees. 'You are my Lord and my God!' he declared.

'Thomas, you believe because you can see me,' said Jesus, 'but how happy people will be who believe in me but have not seen me!'

Later, some of the friends went home to Galilee. One night they went fishing but caught nothing. At daybreak someone on the shore

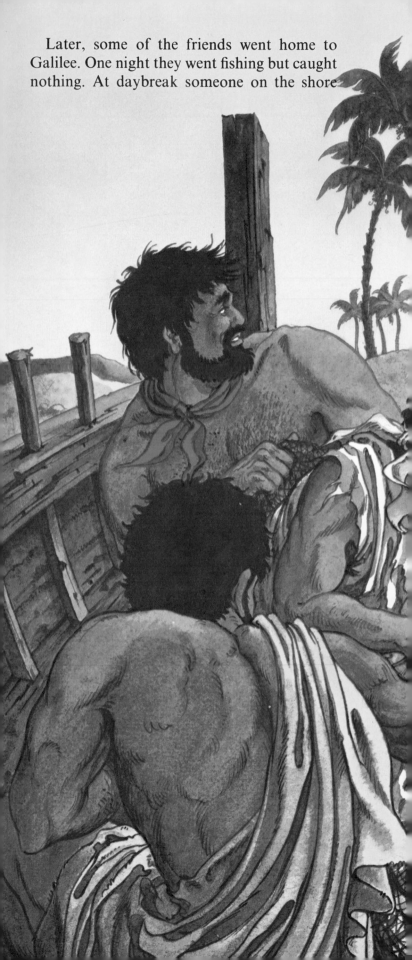

called, 'Throw out your net to the right!' They did so, and at once the net filled with fish.

'That's Jesus!' John told Peter. Peter leapt into the sea. On shore Jesus had a fire blazing and fish ready cooked. 'Bring some more fish,' he said. Peter went back and hauled the heavy net ashore.

'Breakfast's ready!' Jesus called.

After breakfast Jesus asked Peter quietly three times: 'Do you love me?'

'Yes, Lord,' answered Peter, but he remembered how he had let Jesus down.

'Then look after my followers,' said Jesus. Now Peter knew that Jesus still trusted him.

Soon, the time came for Jesus to go back to heaven to be with God. One day he and his close friends went out of the city. They climbed a hill. Jesus prayed that his friends would always know God's love and peace.

'You must tell everyone the good news,' Jesus said. 'I am alive for ever, and I shall be with you always, right to the end of time, just as I told you.'

Then Jesus disappeared from their sight. They would not see him again on earth, but they knew that the Holy Spirit would come and help them.

They returned to Jerusalem and went to the Temple every day to thank God for Jesus. They knew God had sent him to die and come to life again so that everyone who believed in him could be freed from the power of wrong-doing, death and evil.

'Jesus is alive!' they sang, knowing that from then on the whole world would be different.

More than two thousand years have gone by since Jesus met Mary in the Garden of Gethsemane. Still people say – 'Jesus is alive!' Every year at Easter time special services are held to celebrate Jesus' coming to life again. They are happy services. The churches are bright with flowers and glad with happy voices singing. Different countries have their own customs. In Poland, for example, trumpets blow early on Easter morning and church bells ring, telling the waking world that Jesus is alive. In Russia people greet each other with the words: 'The Lord is risen!' and the reply: 'He is risen indeed!'

When the first followers of Jesus knew that he was alive they stopped being sad and frightened. They became happy and very brave. They had to be brave because often they were attacked and hurt by people who did not want them to follow Jesus. You will be able to read about some of the things that happened to them in other Ladybird Bible story books.

It was not only the first Christians who had to be brave. All through the years people who follow Jesus have had to face troubles and difficulties, but because they know Jesus in a special way they have been glad and happy to do so. See if you can find out about some of these people, using the books in your local library to help you. Here are some names to